INVESTIGATING HISTORY

Life in TUDOR & STUART Times

Fiona Goodman and Peter Kent

SIMON & SCHUSTER
EDUCATION

First published in 1991 by
Basil Blackwell Ltd
Reprinted 1991

Reprinted in 1992, 1993 (twice) by
Simon and Schuster Education

Simon & Schuster Education
Campus 400
Maylands Avenue
Hemel Hempstead
Herts HP2 7EZ

British Library Cataloguing in Publication Data
Goodman, Fiona
Life in Tudor and Stuart Times. – (Investigating history).
  1. Great Britain, history, 1485–1714
  I. Title II. Kent, Peter III. Series 941.05

ISBN 0–7501–0418–X

Designed by Helen Castle
Illustrated by Peter Kent
Printed in Great Britain by
Redwood Books, Trowbridge

Contents

General introduction

Investigating History is a series of photocopiable resources designed to cover the National Curriculum for History at Key Stage 2. The Programmes of Study are covered through the full range of skills required in the Attainment Targets.

The series offers one book for each History Study Unit. Each book contains a general introduction, an historical introduction, 20 units and a set of Resource sheets. A unit consists of a double-page spread of teacher's notes and a pupils' activity sheet which may be photocopied. Each unit presents stimulating activities which encourage a skills-based investigative approach to History.

Listed below are Attainment Targets and the outline for History Core Study Unit 2 – Tudor and Stuart Times.

Attainment Targets:
AT1 Knowledge and understanding of history
AT2 Interpretations of history
AT3 The use of historical sources

Core Study Unit 2:	Units in book
Rulers and court life	1, 2, 9, 10, 12, 14, 16, 17
People in town and country	4, 5, 6, 7, 13, 18, 19
Scientific and cultural achievements	7, 19, 20
Exploration and empire	8, 11
Religious issues	3, 15, 17

USING THE BOOK

The following paragraphs give a brief explanation of how the activity sheets and the different sections in the teacher's notes work.

Activity sheets

In general, the activities are suitable for individual, group or class work. The activity sheets are intended to provide stimuli to both teachers and pupils which may then lead to the development of individual or group historical enquiry. The sheets are not intended to be worked through methodically: teachers will wish to select and adapt the activities and ideas to suit the needs of the children.

The Resource sheets at the back of the book are intended to supplement particular activity sheets; indication is given in the teacher's notes if and when a Resource sheet may be relevant.

Teacher's notes

- The *Skills* section lists the historical skills which the children will be developing in working on the activity sheet.

- The *National Curriculum* charts only indicate the Attainment Targets which will be studied through working on the activity sheet. Attainment targets covered by extension activities and cross-curricular work are not listed in these charts.

- The *Background information* section gives useful historical information, particularly highlighting some areas with which children may be unfamiliar.

- The *Introductory work* section gives suggestions for pre-experience and ways of introducing the sheet.

- The *Using the sheet* section details any equipment children might need, explains what the children are expected to do and suggestions for prompting questions or activities to help them get the most out of the activity sheet.

- The *Extension activities* often include suggestions for cross-curricular activities and ways of developing the skills and knowledge promoted by the activity sheet.

Investigating History should not be seen as the entire scheme of work for a project. Children should also have the opportunity to handle and examine artefacts and original documentation and, if possible, to visit sites and museums which will further enrich their studies. They should also have access to research and information books which will allow them to investigate particular areas of interest.

RESOURCES

Pupil information books

'Beginning History' is a series by Wayland which includes titles like *Plague and Fire, The Gunpowder Plot, Tudor Sailors, Tudor Towns*
'Living History' is a series by Wayland which includes the title *The Tudors*
Finding out about Tudor Law and Order, M Jones, Batsford
Growing up in Elizabethan Times, A Clarke, Batsford
Growing up in Puritan Times, A Clarke, Batsford
The Illustrated History of the World Vol 5, Simon & Schuster Young Books
James I and the Gunpowder Plot, L Du Garde Peach, Ladybird
The National Trust Book of the Armada, M Connatty, Kingfisher Books
The Tudors and Stuarts, 'Oxford Junior History', Oxford University Press
Tudor Britain, T Triggs, Wayland
Tudor Seafarers, S Butters, Oxford University Press

General introduction

Background/teacher's reference

'Evidence in History' series includes the titles *The Tudors* and *The Stuarts*, Jon Nichol, Simon & Schuster Education

A Teacher's Guide to Using Portraits, S Morris, English Heritage

In Search of History 1485 – 1714, J F Aylett, Edward Arnold

Old World, New World 1480 – 1600, 'History in Action', C Jordan and T Wood, John Murray

Seventeenth Century Food and Cooking, English Heritage

Tudor Times, 'Living in the Past', H. Middleton, Simon & Schuster Education

Historical fiction

A Stone in a Pool, Place Mill, Plain Jane all by Barbara Softly

A Traveller in Time, Alison Uttley

Brother Dusty Feet, Simon, The Witch's Brat all by Rosemary Sutcliffe

Harrow and Harvest, Barbara Willard

Maroon Boy, Robert Leeson

The Children of Green Knowe, Lucy Boston

Posters

Pictorial Charts Educational Trust offer the following posters:

Elizabeth the Queen

Elizabethan Seamen

Families in History: Romans to Victorians

History Timeline: Romans to Victorians

The Civil War

The Elizabethan Court

Computer software

1665 simulates life at time of plague outbreak in London in 1665 (Tressell Publications), BBC

Into the Unknown simulates a voyage of discovery in the 15th century (Tressell Publications), BBC, RML Nimbus

Mary Rose, The Anatomy of a Tudor Warship 1510 – 1988 (CSH), BBC

Models/Packs

Make a Model Galleon, Macdonald

Battlegame Armada (board game), Macdonald

Useful addresses/places to visit

English Heritage Education Service, Keysign House, 429 Oxford Street, London W1R 2HD

Hampton Court Palace, East Molesey, Surrey KT8 9BS

National Maritime Museum, Greenwich, London SE10 9NF

National Portrait Gallery, St Martin's Place, London WC2H 0NE

National Trust, Education Service

Science Museum, Exhibition Road, London SW7 2DD

The Mary Rose Exhibition, Portsmouth Harbour, Portsmouth, Hampshire

Tower of London, London

Historical introduction

In many ways the period of two hundred years spanned by the Tudors and Stuarts is the most exciting and interesting of British history. During that time the country underwent a profound transformation in the worlds of politics, religion, economics, science and art. The two centuries saw six foreign wars, two civil wars and a revolution. One king lost his head, another was expelled in ignominy, one Archbishop of Canterbury was burnt to death, another beheaded and numerous lesser folk lost their lives through principles of religion or politics.

The Tudor and Stuart monarchs themselves match their age, providing enough eccentricity, malevolence and curious twists of personality to keep biographers busy for the forseeable future. Henry VII was a conniving miser, Henry VIII a vindictive, selfish egomaniac, Mary I a religious fanatic and Charles II a spectacular profligate. Only the last two Stuarts, Mary and Anne, were dull.

The rise of the Tudors conveniently coincided with the apparent end of the medieval period. All sorts of institutions were changing at the end of the 15th century and when Henry Tudor killed Richard III, the last Plantaganet, at the Battle of Bosworth in 1485, ending the Wars of the Roses, the new dynasty appears to have ushered in a new age. Henry VII suppressed the great nobles and amassed a large fortune through various dubious methods. When he died in 1509 he bequeathed to his son Henry a firm throne, a prosperous, peaceful country and a large fortune.

The most profound change instituted by Henry VIII was his break with the Roman Catholic Church and the establishment of the Church of England. Although the ideas of the Reformation were current in England, Henry's motives were not specifically religious. He needed a son to ensure an uncontested succession but his wife Catherine of Aragon's one surviving child was a daughter, Mary. Wanting to marry Anne Boleyn, Henry sought a divorce, but the Pope, under pressure from Catherine's uncle, the Emperor Charles V, refused it. Henry solved the impasse by declaring himself head of the Church and granting his own divorce. Then in a move to restore his finances he seized the Church's monastic lands. In 1536 and 1538 all the monasteries were closed and their buildings and land sold.

In the midst of all this turmoil Henry's matrimonial affairs worsened. Anne Boleyn, the cause of so much trouble, disappointed him by bearing another daughter, Elizabeth. Anne was executed on a charge of adultery. Henry then married Jane Seymour, who produced a son, Edward, dying in the process.

The 1540s saw wars with France, Spain and Scotland and when Henry died in 1547 he left an almost bankrupt country riven by religious strife, with a sickly nine-year-old Edward VI on the throne. Edward's reign was marked by the growth of Protestantism and the machinations of the great nobles who controlled the regency. In 1553 Edward died of consumption at the age of sixteen.

An attempt to exclude the Catholic Mary by putting Lady Jane Grey on the throne failed and Mary was crowned in 1553. Mary had three aims: she wished to reunite England with Rome, restore the monastic lands and exterminate Protestants. The first was achieved in 1554, the second never and in her efforts to obtain the third she burnt to death one archbishop, three bishops and at least 274 minor clergy and laypeople, earning herself the title 'Bloody Mary'. She married Philip of Spain, which added xenophobia to the anti-Catholicism of her opponents. Philip dragged England into a war with France in which Calais, England's last continental possession, was lost, and Mary died, childless, unloved and unmourned.

She was succeeded by Elizabeth, who had managed with great skill to keep both her head and her Protestant credentials throughout her sister's reign. Elizabeth was astute and clever enough to ride the storms of her reign; she also avoided the political problems of marrying anyone. The religious problems remained and Elizabeth trod a rigorous middle way between the raging of extreme Protestants or Puritans on one side and Catholics on the other. She was of moderate religious views and had no wish to persecute anybody for a purely spiritual belief. However, her government believed that all Catholics were potential traitors under orders from Rome to depose her in favour of Mary Stuart, her cousin and the deposed Queen of Scotland, so they were persecuted.

In spite of Elizabeth's attempts to avoid conflict, England could hardly stand aside from the great struggle between Protestants and Catholics that was raging throughout the rest of Europe. Outright war with Spain began in 1587. The following year the English fleet defeated the Armada which had been sent to invade. This was the only large-scale action of the conflict. For the rest of her reign Elizabeth did little beyond helping the Dutch against the Spanish and authorising patriotic pirates like Sir Francis Drake to prey on Spanish shipping. The last years of Elizabeth's reign saw an extraordinary flowering of culture, in drama, poetry, architecture, art and music, which has given a gloss to a reign that ended with a very weak government. When she died in 1603 the Tudor dynasty died with her.

Elizabeth's heir was James VI of Scotland, the son of Mary Stuart, whom Elizabeth had had executed in 1587. He became James I of England and for the first time the two kingdoms were united – neither politically nor economically, but by the rather unprepossessing person of the King. James was a complete contrast to Elizabeth, scruffy and with little natural dignity. He believed in the Divine Right of Kings: that his position was derived from God and that to question it was

Historical introduction

tantamount to blasphemy. However, he was sensible enough to keep this theory quiet. He had many good intentions such as ending religious strife, but he achieved little. When he died in 1625 he left a Court with an unsavoury moral reputation, large debts and an unwinnable war with Spain.

His son Charles I was to preside over the most turbulent period of the seventeenth century and was not to survive it. All the religious and political tensions of the previous century erupted and Charles had neither the skill nor judgement to cope. The main issue, complicated by matters of religion, was whether the King should rule alone, consulting Parliament as a matter of condecension, or whether he should be obliged to rule with Parliament. Charles I ignored this problem by ruling without one for most of the 1630s.

After a war with Scotland, fought to enforce the use of the Church of England prayer book, ended in utter fiasco, Charles was forced to call a Parliament which agreed to fund him in return for limitations on his power. There was then a period of confused and frantic politicking before war broke out between the King and his Parliament in 1642. In general, Puritans and the merchant classes supported Parliament while the gentry and the country dwellers supported the King. This left Parliament in control of London and the rich and populous south-east while the King held sway in the poorer north and west.

Both sides improvised armies which fought across the country until the King was finally defeated at Naseby in 1645. Parliament was lucky to have an outstanding general in Oliver Cromwell and the great financial resources of London to equip its army. In 1646 Charles surrendered to a Scottish army who handed him over to Parliament.

While Charles was in captivity the victors wrangled and in 1648 there was a short second civil war. The Royalists were again defeated, leaving the Parliamentary army the most powerful political force in the country, but there was still no satisfactory solution to the original constitutional problems.

An exhausted Parliament realised the futility of all their efforts and considered capitulating to the King and bringing him back on his own terms to restore order and peace. The only other alternative was to get rid of him altogether. A majority of Parliament and the country were for the former, but although only a minority led by the army wanted the latter, the measures were forced through. Charles was deposed, charged with making war on his own people, found guilty and on 30 January 1649 beheaded outside his own palace in Whitehall.

From 1649 to 1660 England was a republic. Monarchy, the House of Lords and the Anglican Church were all abolished. The government was ostensibly the increasingly ineffective Parliament, but real power was held by the army led by Cromwell. In 1653 Cromwell was proclaimed Lord Protector and

Head of State. Britain was now effectively a military dictatorship.

The Puritans who had been persecuted under Charles now sought to impose their view of religious orthodoxy. They were particularly severe on public expressions of enjoyment, and the theatres and bear pits were closed – although, as Macaulay wrote about the latter, not because of the pain endured by the bear but because of the pleasure enjoyed by the spectators. Maypoles, the focus of not completely innocent diversions, were felled. Christmas and Easter were deemed idolatrous feasts and struck from the calendar.

The Commonwealth, as the republic was known, outlived its founder by little more than a year. Cromwell's son Richard succeeded him but was unable to control the army, which split into quarrelling factions. Eighteen months after Cromwell's death one section under General Monck decided that the Commonwealth was over and recalled Charles II in 1660.

As if in reaction to the drab years of puritanical rule, Charles and his Court did much to redress the balance. The Restoration was a time when theatres reopened with comedies that have become a byword for cynical, amoral wit, and it became, in some circles, almost a political statement to be as dissolute as possible. Charles's main passions were not intellectual but he dabbled in science and founded the Royal Society. During his reign great advances were made in astronomy, optics, botany and chemistry and Newton laid the mathematical proofs for the inexorable laws governing the motion of the universe.

Charles owned to 17 illegitimate children but not one legitimate son and thus was succeeded by his brother James in 1685. James was a staunch Catholic, but this was tolerated for he had no son and would be succeeded by his impeccably Protestant daughter Mary who was married to William of Orange of the Netherlands. But James, unlike his brother, was a man of principle. He stated that he wished to raise the Catholic Church to equal status with the Church of England. This united against him virtually everyone from Archbishop of Canterbury to Anabaptist cobbler. After James's second wife bore a son there loomed the prospect of a whole dynasty of Catholic monarchs stretching into the future.

William determined to protect what he saw as his wife's rightful inheritance and in November 1688 landed with a Dutch army at Torbay. Hardly a shot was fired. The army deserted James who fled to France, never to return, and William and Mary became joint sovereigns. This was the Glorious Revolution.

William was chiefly interested in his continental struggle with Louis XIV and he was not very popular in England. Mary died in 1694 and William ruled alone until 1702. When he died the throne passed to

Historical introduction

Anne, James's second daughter. She was the last of the Stuarts and her only real claim to fame stems from the happy accident of her reigning during one of the finest periods of English domestic architecture, giving her name to a style. It was said that there was 'only one person in the Kingdom more stupid than she – and that was her husband, Prince George of Denmark'. The main event of her reign, apart from the interminable continental wars, was the parliamentary union of England and Scotland that James I had desired 100 years before. None of Anne's children survived to succeed her and the throne passed to her distant relative, the Elector of the German state of Hanover, who became George I, the first of the Hanoverians. Such was the antipathy of the British to a Catholic king that they preferred an obscure German with hardly a word of English to any of the remaining Stuarts kicking their heels in exile.

Activity Sheets
and
Teacher's Notes

1 The Tudors and Stuarts

Teacher's notes

Skills

Chronological ordering
Making a timechart

Attainment targets

Level	AT 1	AT 2	AT 3
2	↓		
3			
4			
5			

Introductory work

Talking about the children's own knowledge of kings and queens could be a good starting point. They might firstly think of kings and queens in fairy tales. This could initiate a useful discussion about whether they think those monarchs are real or imaginary. How do we know whether they are fictional or real, historical characters? The children could then list the kings and queens they think are real. They will probably name Queen Elizabeth II. What job does she do? Why do we have a queen today? Who was the monarch before her? Who will be the next monarch?

It would be useful to do some pre-activities to help children place the Tudors and Stuarts in time. This could be done by unravelling a toilet roll, each piece representing ten years. The children will quickly see how long ago Tudor and Stuart times were!

Why were the kings and queens called 'Tudors and Stuarts'?

Using the sheet

The easiest way for the children to unjumble the pictures is to cut them up and arrange them on a strip of coloured paper. They can then be stuck down to make a timeline. The dates may be difficult for them to grasp and it would be useful to talk about this before they attempt the sheet. They could make wall displays of their royal timeline to use as a reminder when working on Tudors and Stuarts.

Extension activities

1 Work out how long each monarch ruled. Who ruled the longest/ shortest? What do the children think are the reasons why some ruled for a long time and some only for a short time? When did they stop ruling? Who took over then? (When they died a son/daughter would take the throne.) How long has Queen Elizabeth II been on the throne?

2 A class timeline could be made showing all the kings and queens. As the topic progresses other dates can be added. Unlike the children's own ordering of the pictures, this timeline should be evenly spaced on a scale to be decided.

3 How do the pictures make the characters appear? Children could make up nicknames for them, e.g. James the sly and shifty. This sort of activity should include some discussion about artists' interpretations of a subject.

4 The pictures show changes in fashion and hairstyles. What do the children think of these? They could make a fashion magazine after doing some more research. You could ask them to draw a picture of our queen. How do her hairstyle and outfits compare?

5 There is a gap between 1649 and 1660 which the children will spot. Ask the children to speculate why. They could investigate what was going on during these 11 years.

10

The Tudors and Stuarts

These are pictures of the kings and queens of Tudor and Stuart times. The dates show when they reigned.
Cut the pictures out and put them in order, from earliest to latest times. Then colour them in.

James II
1685–1688

Elizabeth I
1558–1603

Henry VIII
1509–1547

James I
1603–1625

Charles II
1660–1685

Edward VI
1547–1553

Mary I
1553–1558

Henry VII
1485–1509

Charles I
1625–1649

2 Henry VIII

Skills

Using historical evidence
Reconstructing the past from evidence
Chronological ordering
Forming judgements about reliability and value of sources

Attainment targets

Level	AT 1	AT 2	AT 3
2			
3	↓	↓	↓
4			
5			↓

Introductory work

This sheet should be used to help children to understand that there can be more than one version of events or people in the past. A useful introduction for the children might be to talk about evidence, contrasting the sort and amount of evidence we have about someone like Henry VIII with what we have on kings and queens of the 20th century for whom there is far more. You might point out the difference between *primary* and *secondary* evidence (primary evidence is made or written at the time the events happened, secondary evidence is written or produced after the event, e.g. a history reference book).

You could also discuss with the children how reliable they think evidence is? Even if something is written or painted at the time of the event, can we really trust it to be a true version of what happened? Relate this issue to an up-to-date situation like a fight in the playground. If you ask four children to give an account of what happened, you will probably get four different versions of the fight!

Using the sheet

The sheet contains written, pictorial and 'hearsay' evidence about Henry VIII. Using this and the information on the timeline the children need to build up a picture of his life in order to write a life story for the new history book. An alternative means of presentation would be to do a 'This is your Life' book for him or a strip cartoon.

The language used in the written evidence may need discussion as some of the words will be unfamiliar. They should also discuss which pieces of evidence they think are facts and which they think are points of view.

Extension activities

1 Henry's marriages and what happened to his wives is only touched upon in this sheet. The children might investigate this further using reference books. Perhaps they could produce their own portrait gallery of his six wives.
2 The children could cut out a life-size silhouette of Henry at his grossest which could loom over them in the classroom to give a suitable impression of his powerful presence. (The Tower of London armouries should be able to give you Henry's armour measurement.)
3 The children could recreate a Tudor feast with jugglers, a jester and food from Tudor times (recipes can be found in the English Heritage 16th century cookbook – see resources section at the front of this book for their address).
4 Children could discuss how knowing who produced a particular quote or painting might help us decide how 'true' it is. For example, a description of someone written by that persons' known enemy is likely to be derogatory.

Henry VIII

Born — 1490 | Marries 1 · War with France — 1510 | War with France — 1520 | Marries 2 · Marries 3 — 1530 | Marries 4 & 5 · Marries 6 · War with France · Dies — 1540

Here are some pieces of evidence about King Henry VIII.
Look at them carefully. Which are real facts and which say
what people thought about him?

"He is very talented, a good musician. He is a very fine horseman, a good jouster. He speaks French, Latin and Spanish. He is very religious and likes tennis very much."

"His majesty is the most handsome King I have ever seen. He is above the usual height, with an extremely fine calf to his leg. He has a round face so very beautiful that it would become a pretty woman."

The Act of Supremacy, 1534. A law making the King Head of the Church of England.

This is an old rhyme about what happened to Henry's wives. 'Divorced, beheaded died. Divorced, beheaded survived.'

Henry at his new castle at Southsea

1515

1540

Henry's armour in the Tower of London

A new history book about Tudor kings and queens is being
written. Write a life story of Henry to go in the new book. Use
pictures to show some of the things that happened to him.

© Fiona Goodman and Peter Kent. Simon & Schuster Education. 1991.

3 Religious change

Skills

Identifying and describing changes over a period of time
Identifying different types of cause and consequence

Attainment targets

Level	AT 1	AT 2	AT 3
2			
3			↓
4			
5	↓		

Background information

The religious changes which took place during the Tudor and Stuart times are very complex and the official religion of England changed from Catholic to Protestant and back again several times, depending on who was in power. This sheet explores the change from Catholicism to Protestantism, which began when Edward VI (Henry VIII's son) became king and was further reinforced by Elizabeth I. Between these two monarchs came Mary I who was a Roman Catholic.

With the change from Catholicism to Protestantism links with Rome were ended, links that extended back nearly one thousand years. This began in Henry VIII's reign when Parliament announced that he was the Supreme Head of the Church of England, not the Pope. One aspect of this break with Rome is evident in the change from Latin services and writings to English. This is shown on the sheet.

Introductory work

The children may be unfamiliar with the inside of a church so some introductory work on what is found in a church might be useful, particularly the names of things, e.g. altar, lectern.

Using the sheet

The first change the children should notice is the plainness of the lower picture compared to the rich Catholic interior. Other things they should look out for are listed below:

Catholic	Protestant
Latin wording	English wording
Painted walls	Plain walls
Decorated altar	Bare table
Stained-glass windows	Plain glass
Statues	No statues

Extension activites

1 It would be useful for children to visit a local church so they could draw a similar view of the altar area, looking at details that are on the sheet. Perhaps they could visit both Catholic and Protestant churches to see if the differences shown on the sheet are still around today.

2 To give a visual impression of what the churches might have looked like inside you could temporarily divide the classroom into two and strip all the pictures and decorations from the walls on one side, leaving displays etc. up on the other side. The contrast should be quite dramatic!

3 There are further areas of religious life that the children could follow up and research for themselves, e.g. life in a monastery, the closing down and destruction of the monasteries or the importance of religion at school.

Religious change

When I was a child I went to a church like this.

By the time I had grown up, the church had changed and now looks like this.

PRAISE YE THE LORD

SANCTUS SANCTUS SANCTUS

Look carefully at these two pictures of the church. Make a list of things that changed and things that stayed the same. Try to find out about why these changes took place.

4 Rich and poor

Skills

Indentifying cause and consequence
Identifying similarities and differences between past and present

Attainment targets

Level	AT 1	AT 2	AT 3
2			
3	↓		
4			
5			

Introductory work

A good starting point would be to discuss with the children what they think 'Rich' and 'Poor' mean. In Tudor and Stuart times the gulf between the two was much wider than it is today, particularly as the poor received no state help or benefit. The problem of the poor was further accentuated by the closure of the monasteries by Henry VIII, as the monks had previously looked after the poor. In contrast, the children might consider who 'looks after' the poor today.

Beggars or vagabonds, as they were called, lived in shacks or roamed the country looking for work, often with their families. At the opposite end of the scale, rich land-owning families and royalty led a life of luxury and excess.

Using the sheet

Before drawing pictures of the modern equivalents in the chart, the children should compare the differences between rich and poor in Tudor times. They could discuss the differences in small groups. They should try to identify what is going on in each picture. The pictures could even be cut out and muddled up and the children asked to put them in their original groups. Children could do both modern rich and poor equivalents if they wish. The activity sheet asks for the children's own pictures to allow teachers to raise issues of rich and poor today only if they wish to do so.

Children should also be encouraged to discuss the way some things have changed and some have remained the same since Tudor times, e.g. people still dance and play skittles for fun.

Extension activities

1 Children could design and make a board game based on the idea of being either rich or poor in Tudor times. They could design variations based on information from the sheet and further research.

2 Beggars had different ways of begging and so were given different nicknames, e.g. Tom O'Bedlam Angler, Clapperdudgeon. This is a description of a clapperdudgeon: 'He walked round in dirty rags and put arsenic on his to skin to make it bleed. The dirt would make the skin even sorer; in this way he hoped to get money as people would feel so sorry for him.'

Children could draw their own impression from this description and investigate other types of beggars and how they got their names.

3 You could ask children to imagine that they are living in Tudor and Stuart times. They are poor country children and they swop places with rich children for a day. They should do some background reading to help them with their stories. They should say how they feel about going back to their old lives. They should be encouraged to think of reasons other than wealth which made country life different.

Rich and poor

There were very big differences between rich and poor people in Tudor times. Look at the pictures below and compare them. Do we still do or have any of the same things?
Fill in the 'Today' column with pictures of what each of the things is like for you.

	The rich	The poor	Today
Houses			
Clothes			
Fun			
School			
Food			
Work			
Health			
Travel			

© Fiona Goodman and Peter Kent. Simon & Schuster Education. 1991.

5 Crime and punishment

Skills

Using historical evidence
Identifying differences between past and present
Empathising with people of the past

Attainment targets

Level	AT 1	AT 2	AT 3
2	↓		↓
3			
4			
5			

Background information

Many of the punishments used in the Middle Ages, e.g. the ducking stool, the stocks and pillory, being burnt to death, were all still being used in Tudor times. Torture was also used frequently to extract information, especially if you ended up in the Tower of London. There was no police force nor were there fair trials with juries. The local Justice of the Peace ran what we would call magistrate's courts. Aldermen or councillors would form a court for minor offences. Very serious crimes like murder and treason were reserved for the king's judges who sat permanently in London and went out into the country to hold assizes, every three months.

Introductory work

Keeping law and order in Tudor times was often harsh and unfair, or so it seems to us living in the 20th century. As an introductory discussion the children could list the sort of crimes that take place today and how people are punished for them. Prison and fining will emerge as the two main punishments used and will contrast well with the variety and harshness of punishment 500 years ago.

Using the sheet

The activity is split into two parts. Firstly, they should rank the punishments in order of 'worst' to 'best' and secondly they should do the same for the crimes written in the judge's book. The children might like to tabulate the information like this:

Punishments in order with worst first

Letter	Description
G	Burnt at stake

Crimes in order with worst first

Name	Crime
John Hall	Being drunk and singing

You could ask the children to spot the spelling 'mistakes' (old-fashioned spellings) in the judge's book, or any other words they don't recognise.

Extension activities

1 The children could consider how each crime in the judge's book might be punished today. Would any of them not be considered a crime today?
2 Children could invent a set of ten Tudor laws based on the crimes committed. They might like to write them up as a poster to be put up in the town using 'olde English' handwriting and language.
3 Children could write the story of one of the character's crimes and the punishment she/he ended up with as if they were that character.

Crime and punishment

In Tudor times people who broke the law were cruelly punished. Look at pictures A–G. Put the punishments in order from the most to the least cruel.

Agnes Goodbody
Nicholas Bacon
Richard Norton
John Hall
Sir Robert Dannet
Basil Blackwell
Will Sykes

Speaking ill of her neighbour
Fighting in ye street
Theft of apples
Being very drunk and singing
Plotting against Her Majestie
Heresy (wrong religious ideas)
Murder and robberie

The judge's book has names of lawbreakers and their crimes. Put the crimes in order with the worst one first and so on. Match a punishment from the pictures above with each of the crimes.

6 The market

Skills

Identifying differences between past and present
Analysing different features of an historical situation
Assessing how different features of an historical situation relate to each other

Attainment targets

Level	AT 1	AT 2	AT 3
2			
3			
4			
5			

Background information

The market place would have been the hub of activity in a Tudor town. It would have been a noisy, smelly, busy place where the ordinary people of the town and surrounding villages would meet to buy and sell provisions. Like some modern markets, different trades would be grouped together and as well as the more familiar food stalls there would have been a whole variety of different trade stalls, some of which would be unfamiliar to us today, like glovers, tanners, weavers, drapers, cappers (cap makers), dyers, coopers (barrel makers), mercers (textile dealers), wagonmakers, blacksmiths, shoemakers.

Introductory work

As an introductory activity children might consider what stalls and trades there are in a modern market, why people go to markets, and what the atmosphere is like in markets. They might also discuss the way country folk came into town markets to buy and sell their goods in Tudor times. Does this still go on today?

Using the sheet

It might be useful to read through the rule list as a larger group. Children could think about why they had certain laws and what those laws meant. Do modern markets have rules?

The task of producing a report for the inspector could be done as a group activity and include writing and drawings.

There is a lot of detail in the picture on the activity sheet and children should be encouraged to consider the different aspects of the situation, e.g. clothes, buildings, food, goods. How do these different features relate to each other? For example, the country folk selling vegetables show how farming life in the country related to market life in towns.

Extension activities

1 The Inspector of Markets has asked each stallholder to produce a sign advertising what they sell/do. Ask the children to help the stallholders with these.
2 Children could imagine they are a visitor from the country making their first outing to a busy town market.
3 Children who have been to a market will be familiar with the shouting and calling that goes on as stallholders try to sell their wares. Ask them to make up similar calls for the traders in the Tudor market.
4 Further research could be done into trades and occupations in the local area in Tudor times. You might find surveys and tax lists of your local town dating back to the 1500s and 1600s in your local records/archive offices. You might want to enter this sort of information onto a data-handling computer program, which will allow easy access and classification.
5 Children could do a wall display showing differences/similarities in markets then and now.

The market

In the 1500s and 1600s most people did their shopping in the market place of their local town.

Market Rules
1 No trading before 6 o'clock.
2 All food to be sold at the price set by the Mayor.
3 No bad or stale food to be sold.
4 All weighing scales must be marked with the Mayor's seal.
5 No rubbish.
6 No games.
7 All smelly trades to be in one place.
8 All goods to be sold from stalls only.
9 No beggars.
10 All stalls to pay a toll and display a seal.

The Inspector of Markets needs to know if any rules are being broken in this market. Look closely at what is going on in the market and write a report to help him.

7 Entertainments

Skills

Identifying differences between past and present
Using historical evidence
Empathising with people of the past

Attainment targets

Level	AT 1	AT 2	AT 3
2	↓		↓
3			
4			
5			

Introductory work

In Tudor times most people made their own entertainment. If you lived in or near a large town there would be some public entertainments on offer. Children will recognise that this is still true today – there are usually more amenities in towns than there are in the country. It would be helpful if they could look at samples of local entertainment guides. Children could also discuss what sort of entertainments we have today that weren't around 500 years ago. You could ask a senior citizen to come in and talk about how people entertained themselves when she/he was young. This will help children understand that televisions, videos and the cinema are all fairly new forms of entertainment.

Using the sheet

The sheet gives just four examples of the sorts of entertainment on offer in Tudor times. What do the children think was involved in each? The activity of writing an entertainment guide could be tackled by a group of four children, each writing about one of the entertainments which could then be collated in a guide book or as a newspaper page on entertainment (all set in Tudor times).

The children may want to cut out the pictures on the sheet to use in their guide.

Extension activities

1 Further research could be done into Shakespeare and the theatre. The most famous theatre was The Globe in London where Shakespeare's plays were performed. In smaller towns, travelling players would put up an improvised stage. Play going was very popular.

   Children could make a model of the Elizabethan theatre. This work should involve some discussion of the idea that plays are another way in which past events are represented.
2 Children could discuss the morality of bear baiting. Does anything like this take place today?
3 Children could try to imagine they are a Tudor child living in the countryside. How would they entertain themselves with no television or books? Perhaps they could make up their own game for a group of six friends?

22

Entertainments

Mary and Thomas live in a Tudor town. They want to know what they can do for fun. Write or draw an entertainment guide for them.

A dance

Bear baiting

Football

The theatre

Prices
Seat on
Stage 5p
Seat in
gallery 3p
Stand in
pit 1p

HAMLET
by
William Shakespeare

Which of these do we have today? Which would you choose?

8 Drake's voyage

Skills

Using historical evidence
Evaluating historical evidence
Empathising with people of the past

Attainment targets

Level	AT 1	AT 2	AT 3
2	↓		
3			
4			
5			↓

Background information

When Francis Drake set sail around the world in 1577 he was already a sea captain of note, having made a lot of money through sinking Spanish ships and plundering their booty, and journeying to the New World (America). As well as discovering new routes and new places, Drake hoped his world voyage would bring back further wealth through raids and plunder.

Life at sea at this time was dreadful; diseases like scurvy and plague were commonplace, fresh food and water ran out very quickly, living conditions were cramped, punishments were cruel and the ships were at the mercy of terrible weather conditions.

To give children an idea of what the ships were like, it would be useful to show them a picture of a sailing ship of the time and talk about some of its shortcomings. Children could compare it with a modern liner or tanker.

Using the sheet

The information on the sheet is presented as Drake's diary. Diaries are an important form of primary evidence. Diaries are only one person's view of events but often contain a large amount of information about the past. Children might be able to bring in diaries of grandparents or the teacher could read an extract from a diary that has been made into a book, e.g. *The Diary of Anne Frank*, Roald Dahl's *Boy*.

The children will need a copy of Resource sheet 2 (map of the world) on which to plot the route. Because the names of places have changed since Drake's time, children will need to use the longitude and latitude directions to find out where he is at each point. It is unlikely that children will be familiar with longitude and latitude so you may wish to go over this before starting the sheet. Some preliminary work using a children's atlas and basic coordinates would be useful.

The children should mark on each point when each diary entry was made. If they join them up Drake's route will be revealed! They could then look more closely at what happened on the journey. They could invent symbols to add to their maps to represent some of the things that happened on Drake's trip.

Extension activities

1 Drake mentions some place names in his diary. Using a modern map, can the children work out the modern place names of where he travelled?
2 Using the scale on a modern map can the children work out how far Drake travelled and how long each stretch of the voyage took (use the dates for the diary entries).
3 Children could design a poster asking for sailors to join Drake's trip around the world. They should think about why sailors might want to join the journey.
4 Old maps of the world can be fascinating. They show different views of how people thought the world looked. Children could compare an old map with a modern map, and/or try to follow Drake's route on the old map.

Drake's voyage

In 1577 Francis Drake set out to sail around the world. He kept a diary of his journey. Here are some of the things he wrote.

15 November 1577. Latitude 50° N, Longitude 5° W.
We set sail from Plymouth with five ships and 164 men.

30 March 1578. Latitude 10° S, Longitude 25° W.
There has been no wind for the past three weeks. But there has been terrible lightning and thunder. We have not run short of food because many flying fish fall into our ships.

25 April 1578. Latitude 35° S, Longitude 55° W.
We entered the great River Plate where we filled our barrels with fresh water.

6 September 1578. Latitude 55° S, Longitude 70° W.
After 16 days sailing we entered the Pacific Ocean.

1 March 1579. Latitude 0°, Longitude 80° W.
We crossed the Equator and in the afternoon captured a great ship full of treasure called the Cacafuego. We are rich!

3 June 1579. Latitude 40° N, Longitude 125° W.
We sailed into a great and fair bay. I put up a brass plate calling the place New Albion.

9 January 1580. Latitude 0°, Longitude 125° E.
After sailing west across the Pacific Ocean we came to the Moluccas. We stuck fast on a rock. We made the ship lighter by throwing out some of the cargo. A gale blew us off into the sea again.

18 June 1580. Latitude 35° S, Longitude 20° E.
We passed the Cape of Good Hope.

3 November 1580. Latitude 50° N, Longitude 5° W.
We arrived in England with only 56 men and one ship, the Golden Hind.

Plot the route of Drake's journey on your map of the world.

© Fiona Goodman and Peter Kent. Simon & Schuster Education. 1991.

9 Defences against the Armada

Skills

Using historical evidence
Making deductions from evidence
Empathising with people of the past

**Attainment
targets**

Level	AT 1	AT 2	AT 3
2			↓
3			
4			
5			

**Background
work**

The Armada, a fleet of 110 fighting ships, 40 supply ships and 30,000 soldiers and sailors, set sail for Britain in July 1588. The decision to send the Armada was made by King Philip II of Spain in response to constant plundering of Spanish ships by English sea captains, and in the hope that Catholicism might be restored to England.

**Using
the sheet**

As an introduction to the Armada the children might look at a map of Europe and follow the route taken by the Armada from Spain to England. The activity sheet presents an imaginary scenario of a Spanish spy working out the best places for the Armada to land so it would probably be better to do this sheet before finding out what the fate of the Armada was. The next unit on excavating the wreck of a ship from the Armada gives some clues as to what happened!

The children could locate the area of the map shown on the sheet on a map of Great Britain. However, what is most significant is the set of features of the area – the forts, castles and camps, and the natural features that might influence the choice of landing place. Rather than giving the children a completely free choice the sheet gives them five possible landing places which need to be discussed before they decide on the best place. The activity would be best done in small groups as a discussion activity with one child in each group recording the pros and cons of each landing place. The group should then come to a final decision and present their choice to the rest of the class, giving reasons for that choice.

They might like to make their own version of the spy's report making it look as authentic as possible.

**Extension
activities**

1 Children could investigate what actually happened when the Armada arrived in the English Channel and what the outcome of the expedition was. After researching from reference books they could present the information as a strip cartoon or on a map showing what happened where or as a newspaper front page or series of headlines.

2 A medal was made in celebration of the victory of the English over the Spanish. The children could design and make their own medal, based on information they find in reference books or primary sources.

(See list of resources suggested on pages 4 and 5.)

Defences against the Armada

I have studied the coast from London to Brighton to find the best place for the Spanish army to land. The English coast is very strongly defended by gun batteries ⚙, forts 🏰 and castles 🏯. There are also cliffs ⛰ and marshes to cross 〰. There is a camp of 10,000 men at Tilbury. I looked at the five possible landing places marked on the map. The best place to land is _____ I hope this letter will help you make your final plan.

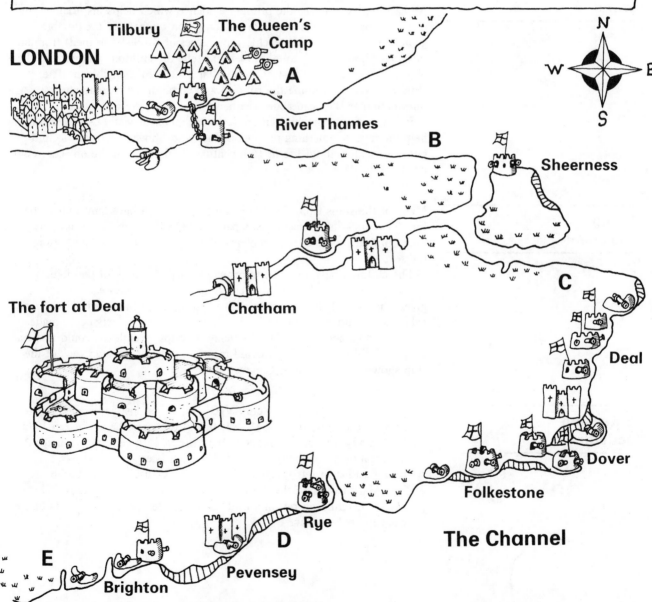

Unfortunately the important bit of the Spanish spy's report was burnt by a candle. Look at each landing place A to E. For each place write down the good and bad points about landing there. Which landing place do you think the spy chose?

© Fiona Goodman and Peter Kent. Simon & Schuster Education. 1991.

10 Armada wreck

Skills

Using historical evidence
Reconstructing the past from evidence
Evaluating evidence

Attainment targets

Level	AT 1	AT 2	AT 3
2			↓
3			
4			
5			↓

Introductory work

The importance of evidence and the rôle of the archaeologist in uncovering evidence are the main subjects of this activity sheet. Archaeologists discover the primary evidence which helps historians write history books. As an introductory activity you might play the dustbin game with the class. The teacher puts pieces of rubbish (cleaned) from an imaginary household into a binliner and tells the children that each of the objects is a clue to the sort of family that generated the rubbish. The children have to examine the rubbish and come up with as much information as they can about the family.

In this activity the children are acting as archaeologists, using clues to help them find something out just as Pick and Shovel are trying to find out information about life in 16th-century England from the objects found on the Armada wreck.

Using the sheet

Many of the ships from the Armada were sunk and have lain undisturbed for 400 years – an archaeologist's paradise! Children could discuss what they think are some of the problems of excavating a ship at the bottom of the sea.

The children have to make information cards for each of the objects on the sea floor. They should think carefully about the clues each object gives; the plan of the ship should also help them in their deductions. An exhibition could be mounted in the classroom, with objects being made out of card/papier mâché/clay/Plasticine. Groups of children could make a couple of objects each. They could make a model of the side view of the ship showing where the objects were found.

Extension activities

1   The Mary Rose, one of Henry VIII's warships, lost as it sailed out of Portsmouth harbour in 1545, was finally raised to the surface in 1982. It gave a wealth of information about life in 16th-century England. An information pack about the Mary Rose has been produced (see resources list in introduction) which provides useful information.
2   The Mary Rose and the Armada wreck are like time capsules. What would the children put in a time capsule to tell people 500 years hence what life is like now?

Armada wreck

After they lost the battle, the ships in the Spanish Armada set sail for home. Many of them were wrecked in a storm. They ended up at the bottom of the sea.

Now this looks interesting. I wonder what it is?

blub

blub

Professor Pick and Dr. Shovel are planning to give a show of the objects that they find. Help them by making information cards for each object. These cards should say what the object is and where it might have been used on the ship.

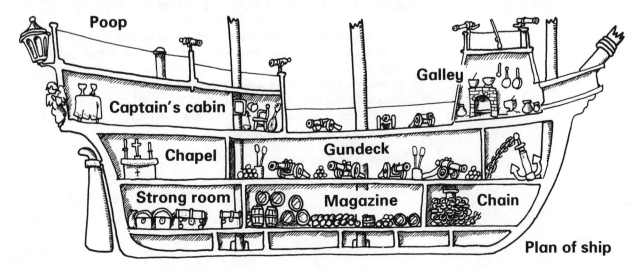

Poop

Galley

Captain's cabin

Chapel

Gundeck

Strong room

Magazine

Chain

Plan of ship

11 Sir Walter Raleigh

Skills

Empathising with people of the past
Using historical evidence
Making deductions from evidence

Attainment targets

Level	AT 1	AT 2	AT 3
2	↓		↓
3			
4			
5			

Background information

Sir Walter Raleigh was a well-known sea captain of the 16th and 17th centuries. On his travels he discovered such things as the potato and tobacco and brought them back to England. Part of his motivation in sending out a colony of people to America was to exploit the natural resources of North America and further enlarge the English Empire. He decided to call the colony Virginia, after the 'virgin queen' Elizabeth I. In fact, his own attempts to start a colony were unsuccessful and it was not until the Pilgrim Fathers set sail in 1620 in the Mayflower that a permanent colony was established in Virginia.

It may be useful to discuss with the children why they think explorers such as Raleigh and Drake voyaged out and how this led to the creation of the British Empire, the remains of which we have today.

Using the sheet

Pick and Shovel set the scene, presenting two of the things Raleigh brought back from his travels: the potato and tobacco. The children might discuss the dangers we know about cigarette smoking which would not have been known about in Raleigh's time.

The activity to make out a list of supplies that the colonists would take with them will need a lot of discussion, e.g. What would be needed to set up a settlement? What materials might they find over there? They might present their list in writing and/or use diagrams, possibly showing what each item would be used for. The problem of storage on board ship, especially of perishable items, could be a further area of investigation (how are perishable items transported today?).

Extension activities

1 The idea of sailing off to America and setting up a settlement could be extended into rôle-play/drama. How would people be persuaded to join the expedition? What would life be like on board ship? What problems might the settlers face? Will the new settlers need laws? What rôle will each person play in the new settlement?

2 On a modern map of the U.S.A. children could find Virginia and the area covered by the map shown on the sheet. What are the modern names of these places?

3 Before reaching America the families had to endure a long uncomfortable sea journey. Children could investigate conditions on board a ship in the 16th and 17th centuries and write a diary as if they were a child travelling to America.

Sir Walter Raleigh

I have Sir Walter Raleigh to thank for bringing tobacco to Britain. This is what he said about it.

The Indians suck it through pipes of clay.

It is also said that he brought back potatoes from America as well. Just think, we might never have had chips if it wasn't for him.

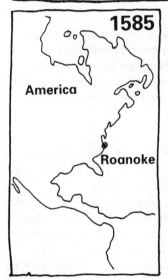

1585

America

Roanoke

The first settlement

Sir Walter Raleigh helped the first English people travel to and settle in America. He sent out 91 men, 17 women and nine children in three small ships. They had to take *everything* with them that they might need to start a new life in America. Make out a list of supplies for Sir Walter to send off with them.

1685

America

English settlements

After 100 years

12 Elizabeth I

Teacher's notes

Skills

Using historical evidence
Making deductions from evidence
Evaluating evidence
Interpreting contradictory evidence
Empathising with people of the past

Attainment targets

Level	AT 1	AT 2	AT 3
2	↓		
3			
4			
5		↓	↓

Background information

For further information about Elizabeth I see the historical introduction on pages 6–8.

This unit explores how evidence about an historical figure can be diverse and contradictory. Versions of the post differ according to the bias of the person who produced that evidence. All the evidence on the sheet is copied from *primary* evidence, evidence produced while Elizabeth was alive. *Secondary* evidence, e.g. history books, films or television programmes, might give a completely different image of Elizabeth. Why?

Introductory work

As an introductory activity you could choose a modern figure, e.g. the Prime Minister or a television personality, and give the children two written accounts which give different views about that person. Discuss how the person might be remembered 500 years hence and which account of the person might be believed. Children could write contradictory accounts for personalities of their choice.

Using the sheet

The two written accounts give two versions of what Elizabeth I looked like. It is important for the children to note who wrote each account and discuss what this tells us, i.e. might that person be biased?

The written accounts contrast well with the portrait and the picture of the unused coin mould. Why do they think the coin mould was not used?

The children are asked to hold an imaginary interview with each of the people who wrote or drew the four images. This can be presented in written form or possibly taped as a 'radio' interview. The activity could be further extended into an imaginary debate between the four people.

Extension activities

1 Children could choose one of the written accounts and draw a portrait of Elizabeth according to the account. Can other children match the portrait to the account?
2 Children could make a material collage/costume doll based on the portrait on the sheet. You could present them with the following scenario:
   'You are an assistant to a costume designer for a new play about Elizabeth. Do some further research and produce an outfit for the Queen and for one of her noblemen, e.g. Raleigh or Drake.'
3 The Tudor and Stuart period produced many portraits and they give fascinating clues into life at that time (see teacher's resource list on page 5). Children could research the portraits that were painted during this period.

32

Elizabeth I

Elizabeth I was Queen of England for 45 years. The sources below show what different people thought she looked like.

"On her head she wore a great red wig. As for her face it is and appears to be very aged. It is long and thin and her teeth are very yellow and unequal... Many of them are missing so that one cannot understand her easily when she speaks quickly."

Written by André Hurault, a French ambassador, in 1597

"She was a lady upon whom nature had given many advantages. She was of medium height and slim. Her hair was pale yellow, her forehead large and fair, her eyes lively and sweet but short sighted, her nose rising in the middle. Her whole face somewhat long but of admirable beauty."

Written by Sir John Hayward, an English knight, in about 1590

The Armada Portrait, 1590

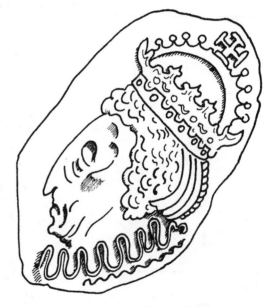

An unused mould for a coin from about 1595

Write out an imaginary interview with each of the people who wrote or drew these images of Queen Elizabeth I. For instance, you could question the coinmaker about why he made the mould like this and why he thinks it was not used.

13 Transport

Skills

Identifying differences between past and present
Describing reasons for an historical development

Attainment targets

Level	AT 1	AT 2	AT 3
2	↓		
3			
4			
5			

Introductory work

How do children think goods were transported in Tudor and Stuart times? The teacher might refer to a timeline showing them how long ago this was, and discuss when they think the engine was invented and how this completely changed methods of transport. You could take a product we use or eat today, e.g. a banana, and look at all the different methods that are used to transport it from source to us. What methods would have been different 500 years ago?

What products might have been transported 500 years ago? How are they different to our needs today? Children could draw up a list of what an ordinary family in Tudor/Stuart times might use and contrast it with what they have in their own homes.

Using the sheet

The children have a choice of four methods and four products. They should be told that they can use more than one method to transport each set of products and they may choose not to use a particular method. They should consider the length of time the journey might take, cheapness, reliability of the chosen method (e.g. Tom might get very tired and have to have a sleep but he would be cheap!). They could record their decisions in a table like this:

Goods	Method of transport	Speed	Cheapness	Reliability
Beer	Dick the carter	7/10	7/10	8/10

The children are also asked to design their own form of transport. They might follow the technology process as set out in the National Curriculum report for Technology: identifying needs and opportunities, generating a design, planning and making, evaluation.

Extension activities

1   If the children make their transport designs into working models, they could plan and carry out tests to see how effective they are, e.g. carrying objects of different sizes and weights, perhaps representing the goods shown on the sheet.
2   Children could make a timeline of transport, past and present, and put forward their own ideas about what future transport will look like.
3   Children could investigate how people travelled in Tudor and Stuart times. They could use old maps of the local town to find out where main roads were, investigate coaching inns and their signs, and work out how long a stage coach might take to do a certain journey compared to a modern fast car.

Transport

Who would you hire to carry each of the different loads to Rivermouth? Design your own form of transport, but remember they had no engines.

14 Gunpowder Plot

Skills

Distinguishing between fact and fiction

Attainment targets

Level	AT 1	AT 2	AT 3
2		↓	↓
3			
4			
5			

Background information

The Gunpowder Plot took place during the reign of James I, the son of Mary Stuart. Often the reason why the plot took place is lost in the story and myth itself. Briefly, James I had ordered Roman Catholic priests to leave England. This greatly angered a small group of Catholics who decided to kill James while he was on business in the House of Parliament.

We have a lot of primary evidence about the Gunpowder Plot which you might want to investigate and use, e.g. prints and pictures of the plotters, a letter sent to Lord Mounteagle warning him to stay away from Parliament, Guy Fawkes' signature.

Using the sheet

It would be useful to look at the top section as a larger group – the children will know about 'fireworks' night on the 5th November and might have heard the 'Remember, remember' rhyme. Find out what they already know about the story. This would be a good point at which to discuss the fact that there are often many different versions of past events and that information about the past is passed on in different ways, e.g. rhymes like 'Remember, remember' or celebrations like Bonfire Night. Some of the words used on the sheet may need some discussion, e.g. treason, plot, Parliament, gunpowder.

The children should then read through the strip cartoon and write their own version of the story. As an alternative, the teacher could read the story to them, and then let them cut out the pieces of the story, jumble them up and rearrange them in the right order.

Treason was regarded as the worst possible crime and the plotters were punished by being hung, drawn and quartered. You could make links here with activity sheet 5 (Crime and punishment) and discuss whether the children think the punishment was a fair one.

Extension activities

1 Children could turn the Gunpowder Plot story into a play or taped radio story.
2 Imagine you are interviewing Guy Fawkes just before his execution. What questions might you ask him? What do you think he would say?
3 Although we know that there was a plot involving a man called Guy Fawkes there is a lot of mystery surrounding the story. Are there any other stories like this (e.g. Robin Hood, King Arthur)? How do we know whether something is fact or fiction?

Gunpowder Plot

Can you help the children remember the story and earn 50 pence? Read the strip cartoon and write down what Tom should say to Professor Pick.

15 The King James Bible

Skills

Using historical evidence
Identifying and describing changes over a period of time
Giving reasons for an historical development

Attainment targets

Level	AT 1	AT 2	AT 3
2			
3			
4			
5			

Introductory work

You could start by looking at a modern Bible, what is in it and how it is set out. If you can get hold of a modern children's Bible and an old standard Bible you could read out different versions of a particular story so the children can see that the old Bible is written in quite a different style. They will see that it is more difficult to understand and this should help them appreciate the changes that took place when James I reformed the Bible in 1611. You could also introduce the word 'translation' and explain what it means before giving them copies of the activity sheet.

Using the sheet

There is a lot of information on this sheet so it might be useful to read it to the class as a group first. In order to do the activity the children will need to understand the information, particularly the changes made to the Bible by James I.

They are asked to design a poster advertising the new Bible, into which should be incorporated details of its new features and an explanation as to why it is so much 'better' than the old version.

Extension activities

1 The original hand-written Bibles are treasured works of art. If the teacher could get hold of a reproduction page of illuminated manuscript the children could refer to this before writing a prayer or verse from the Bible with an italic or quill pen, illuminating the initial letter with colour, pictures, patterns, etc. The Bodleian library in Oxford would be a good source of slides or cards of illuminated manuscripts.
2 The advent of printing marked a great change in the availability of the written word. The first printed weekly newspaper appeared in 1622. Children could choose an event that took place at around about this time and make their own front page, including headlines, a main story, pictures, adverts (e.g. 'New style ruff!', 'Volunteers wanted to sail to America to start new colony'), etc.
3 Children could investigate how printing was carried out before the advent of the printing press and trace the development of the printing press. They could assess whether the development of printing was a gradual or rapid change. Children could experiment with different printing techniques – potato printing, using card cut-outs, lino prints, etc.

The King James Bible

Religion was very important in Tudor and Stuart times. The Bible was the most important book.

Bibles were once copied out by hand so they were very expensive. Very few people could read these bibles because they were in Latin.

At the beginning of Tudor and Stuart times books began to be printed.

In 1611 King James I ordered 47 clever men to rewrite the Bible in English. They did it in a much better way than before. They used the best bits from other people's translations to help them.

The King James Bible became the official Bible used in churches.

Many copies were printed which made them much cheaper.

People could now buy their own copies to read at home.

Imagine you own a bookshop in 1611. Design a poster about the new Bible for your shop window.

16 Civil war

Teacher's notes

Skills

Empathising with people of the past
Interpreting two differing points of view
Being aware of more than one version of the past
Making deductions from historical evidence

Attainment targets

Level	AT 1	AT 2	AT 3
2	↓		↓
3			
4		↓	
5			

Background introductory work

The civil war of 1642 was one of the major events of the Tudor/Stuart period – further information can be found in the historical introduction at the front of the book. Families and villagers were divided in their support for either the King or Parliament and many bloody battles took place. The idea of a war within a country may be difficult for children to understand; you could refer them to the struggle in Northern Ireland between Catholics and Protestants. Or you could explain civil war in terms of a dispute between members of the same class, e.g. one group in the class has been causing problems at break by playing football in the same place as another group who wants to play 'chase'.

Using the sheet

The information at the top of the sheet sets the scene as it was at the beginning of the war. Two children could read the speeches of Colonels Vane and Buskin to the rest of the class (with appropriate fervour) and read out the 'rules' for each side. The children should then decide which side they would like to join, justifying their choice in a letter to their parents.

Using the pictures on the sheet and any other information they find in reference books they could draw a picture of themselves in their new uniform.

Extension activities

1 Children could design their own regimental flag with emblem and motto.
2 Children could look at all the statements on the sheet and decide which are facts and which are points of view, e.g. 'In 1642 civil war broke out in England' is a fact and 'The King knows best' is an opinion.
3 Children could divide into two regiments, elect a colonel each and go out on 'drill' in the playground. This would give them some idea of how difficult it is to get trained and how shambolic the early civil war armies must have been.
4 Children could find out who won the war and write about how they would have felt about the outcome if they were Colonel Vane or Colonel Buskin.

Civil war

In 1642 civil war broke out in England. The quarrel was about whether the King or the Parliament should have the most power. The Cavaliers were on the side of King Charles I. The Roundheads supported Parliament.

Imagine you have run away from home to join the war. Will you join Colonel Vane of the Cavaliers or Colonel Buskin of the Roundheads? Write a letter to your parents to explain your choice. Draw a picture of yourself in your new uniform.

17 The Restoration

Teacher's notes

Skills

Making deductions from historical evidence
Identifying changes over a period of time
Empathising with people of the past

Attainment targets

Level	AT 1	AT 2	AT 3
2			↓
3			
4	↓		
5			

Background information

After the end of the civil war and the death of Charles I, England was left without a king – the only time in the previous 1000 years this had happened. Cromwell ruled the country under the title of Lord Protector. Puritans were in charge and people were made to live simple lives with few luxuries. Some of the forbidden activities included: playing football, drinking in taverns, mending a dress on a Sunday, wearing make-up, swearing. People were punished by whipping or being put in the stocks and were even sent to prison for quite minor offences. The end of Puritanism came with the death of Cromwell in 1658 and the accession of Charles II (son of Charles I) two years later.

Using the sheet

The top section of the sheet gives the children information about the Restoration. You could read this to a larger group and prompt discussion about what changes would have occurred with the end of Puritanism and what people alive at the time would have thought about these changes.

They should then compare the Puritan and Restoration clothes. They could colour them appropriately and choose which they would prefer to wear. They could make a timeline wall display to show changing fashions and include pictures of their modern clothes.

Extension activities

1 You could present the following scenario to the children:
   'You are the costume designer for a new film about the Restoration. Design and make a collage of outfits for a family who lived during this time. You might want to do some further research from reference books to help you.'
2 Children could make up their own 'Snakes and Ladders'-type board game where you climb a ladder if you land on a square that shows a good Puritan act, e.g. 'You name your daughter Patience' or 'You read the Bible every day', and go down a snake if you do something wrong, e.g. 'You wear bright clothes', 'You go to the theatre'.
3 Children could imagine they have just arrived in England in 1657. It is their first visit for ten years. They should write a letter to a friend explaining how different life is compared to the way it was.
4 The children could rename themselves as Puritans, e.g. Fight-the-good-fight, Praise-God, Patience, Modesty, Temperance, Humility (looking up in the dictionary what each of the words mean first!). Take a Puritan register!

42

The Restoration

In 1649 Charles I was killed. For 11 years England had no king and was ruled by Oliver Cromwell. The Puritans were in charge. The Puritans:

closed theatres   **banned bear baiting**   **stopped dancing**   **abolished Christmas!**

In 1658 Oliver Cromwell died. In 1660 Charles II was asked to be King. Charles II was not a Puritan. He liked:

playing cards and gambling   **going to the theatre**   **horse racing**   **dancing and music**

What sort of changes do you think you would have seen if you were alive when Charles II became King?

Puritan clothes

Restoration clothes

In what ways are Puritan clothes different to Restoration clothes? Why do you think they are different? Which would you prefer to wear? How are they different to modern clothes?

18 The Great Plague

Skills

Use of historical evidence
Making deductions from evidence
Empathising with people of the past
Identifying different types of cause and consequence

Attainment targets

Level	AT 1	AT 2	AT 3
2			↓
3	↓		
4			
5	↓		

Background information

The Great Plague of 1665 was caused, as scientists later discovered, by fleas carried in the fur of rats. At the time people thought the plague was a punishment sent from God or was caused by bad air. Sufferers of the plague would first develop a fever accompanied by sickness and/or sneezing fits and a rash of reddish-pink spots. The children's rhyme *Ring a-ring-a-roses* is about the plague.

Thousands of people died, particularly in large cities where street conditions were insanitary. Huge plague pits were dug for the dead bodies, because graveyards filled up very quickly.

Pieces of primary evidence from the time, e.g. written accounts, letters, prints, bill of mortality records, give a lot of information about the plague. These can be found in some of the books listed in the resources section (pages 4 and 5) or in your local records office.

Using the sheet

Pick and Shovel have been called in to look at a plague pit uncovered by builders (this is often the way major archaeological finds are discovered). Dr Shovel provides the answer to what he thinks it is, the children may have other ideas!

The burial scene gives further clues as to what happened and could be discussed by small groups of children.

The main activity asks the children to redraw the Stuart prevention methods in the order they think best and draw two suggestions of their own. Alternatively, they could cut out the pictures of the Stuart methods and order them. This could be done by a small group who would then explain their choice to the rest of the class.

Children might also discuss how they think plague affected people's lives, using the six ways of prevention to help them. They could also talk about how it might have been different for town and country people.

Extension activities

1 Children could write out the rhyme *Ring a-ring-a-roses* and decide what each line is about ('roses' probably means red spots, 'posies' bunches of herbs or spices). This could be illustrated.

2 Decorated playing cards were popular at this time, often depicting contemporary scenes. Children could design the cards for one suit based on scenes from the plague.

3 Further investigation could be done into how the plague affected your local area, using records and other primary source material from your local records office. You might be able to get hold of contempory maps which could be reproduced for children to record the number of deaths and sufferers from the plague. (I.T. data handling and map programs would be useful here to process what might be a large amount of information.)

The Great Plague

Professor Pick and Dr. Shovel have been called to look at a horrible discovery.

Well, what is it then? Is it murder?

No, it's probably a plague pit from the Great Plague of 1665.

There were so many dead that they could not bury them in ordinary graves.

We have a picture from 1665.

In 1665 many people were killed by the Great Plague. These pictures show ways they thought would help them avoid the plague. They are numbered to show which order people tried. 1 is the way they thought would work best. Redraw the pictures in the order you think would work best.

1 Prayer

2 Being good

3 Bonfires in streets

4 No entertainment

5 Lock up people who have the plague

6 Run away to country

19 Fire!

Skills

Use of historical evidence
Making deductions from evidence
Empathising with people of the past
Identifying different types of cause and consequence

Attainment targets

Level	AT 1	AT 2	AT 3
2			
3			↓
4			
5	↓		

Background information

On September 2nd, 1666 the Great Fire of London broke out, partly as a result of the atrocious street conditions that had contributed to the spread of the plague. The fire actually began in a bakery in Pudding Lane and by the time it stopped, nearly a week later, it had destroyed two-thirds of the city of London.

Using the sheet

The picture depicts a city street. You could prompt the children to study the picture by asking: What is the street like? How is it different to the street you live in?

The children are asked to colour the scene using appropriate colours, so they should read the information about what the houses are made of at the top of the sheet.

They will need to look carefully at the picture to spot all the different ways being used to fight the fire. Comparisons could be drawn with fire-fighting methods used today.

For the plan of London activity the children should discuss what is 'wrong' with the old plan and how this might have contributed to the spread of the fire. What do they think made the houses vulnerable to fire? This discussion should help them with their own new plan. (This is probably best done as a group activity.).

Various architects came up with plans for London, e.g. John Evelyn and Christopher Wren. Copies of these plans can be found in the reference books listed in the resource section at the front of the book and these could be compared with the children's own plans.

Extension activities

1 The Fire of London was commemorated in a monument erected near to where the fire started. It is a stone colomn, over 61 metres high. Children could design their own monuments.
2 One result of the fire was that people started to insure their houses with companies who had their own fire engines. Lead fire-marks were fixed to the walls of insured houses. These lead fire-marks often depicted the 'logo' of the company. Children could research what these fire marks looked like from information books and invent their own.
3 Christopher Wren was responsible for the rebuilding of many of London's churches, the most famous being St Paul's Cathedral. Children could investigate his life and work.
4 Children could do an experiment to illustrate how difficult it was to get water to a fire. They could form a bucket chain and see how many litres they could get from a tap to a tub 100 metres away in, say, ten minutes. Then see how long a hose would take!

Fire!

In the 1600s most houses were made of wood with thatched roofs. Houses like this often caught fire. Nearly all of London was burnt down in the Great Fire of 1666.

Colour this picture of a street on fire. Think about what the houses were made of. Make a list of the different ways being used to fight the fire. Which way works best?

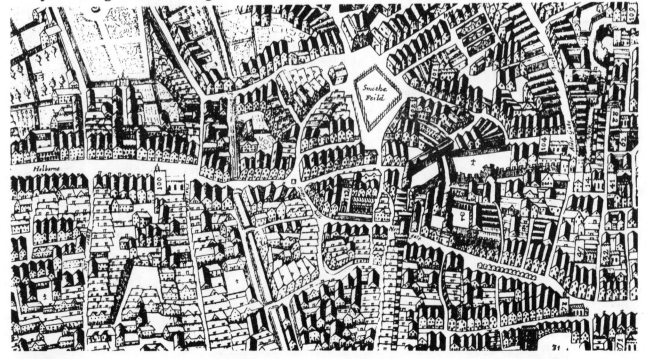

This is a plan of London before the fire. Draw a plan for the new city that you think would be safer. You could think about things like the width of the streets and the number of houses.

Skills

Giving reasons for an historical development

Attainment targets

Level	AT 1	AT 2	AT 3
2			
3	↓		
4			
5			

Background information

The 16th and 17th centuries brought great advances in scientific ideas as scientists began to invent new things rather than just proving old theories. Other scientists of note, apart from Isaac Newton, were Galileo who invented a new telescope and came up with new theories about the earth and sun, and William Harvey who studied the human body.

Using the sheet

Newton's inventions may need some explanation. You could give some practical demonstrations, e.g. reflect white light through a prism to see it split into seven colours. You could also talk about rainbows. You could explain how gravity works by telling the story of the apple falling on Newton's head. You could show them a telescope or a pair of binoculars and discuss how they help us see things a long way away.

The children then have to decide which of the inventions might help the people at the bottom of the sheet and in what way it would help them. A small group of children might further research one of these areas and present their findings back to the rest of the class.

Extension activities

1 Newton's discovery that white light is made up of seven colours could be expanded into several practical science activities, e.g. exploring how light passes through different transparent objects (lenses, colour filters, water, prisms) or making colour spinners. These are basically discs of card, divided into seven, each section coloured one of the seven main colours (violet, indigo, blue, green, yellow, orange, red). You thread string through the centre of the disc and when the string is spun the card rotates very quickly. The colours spinning together gives a whitish tone.

2 Children could trace the development of one invention, e.g. the telescope, through to the present day. The Science Museum or the Royal Observatory at Greenwich would be a good source of information for this. Children could present their findings as an illustrated timeline.

3 This sheet shows some of the inventions of the 17th century. Children could discuss and list things that have been invented in the 20th century. Which of these do they think is the most important and has the greatest effect on our lives today?

Isaac Newton

Isaac Newton was the most famous scientist of his time. He was born on Christmas Day 1642. When he was a boy he made:

a water clock

a self-propelled carriage

furniture for his sister's dolls.

When he was older he continued inventing and discovering things like:

a new way of doing sums (calculus)

the fact that white light is made up of seven colours

the laws of gravity and ideas of mass and force

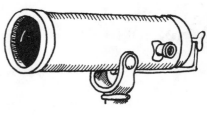

a new sort of telescope.

Which of Isaac Newton's discoveries do you think was the most important? Which discovery/invention do you think most helps the people below?

Artist

Astronaut

Astronomer

Civil war soldiers

A Restoration family

Resource Sheet 2

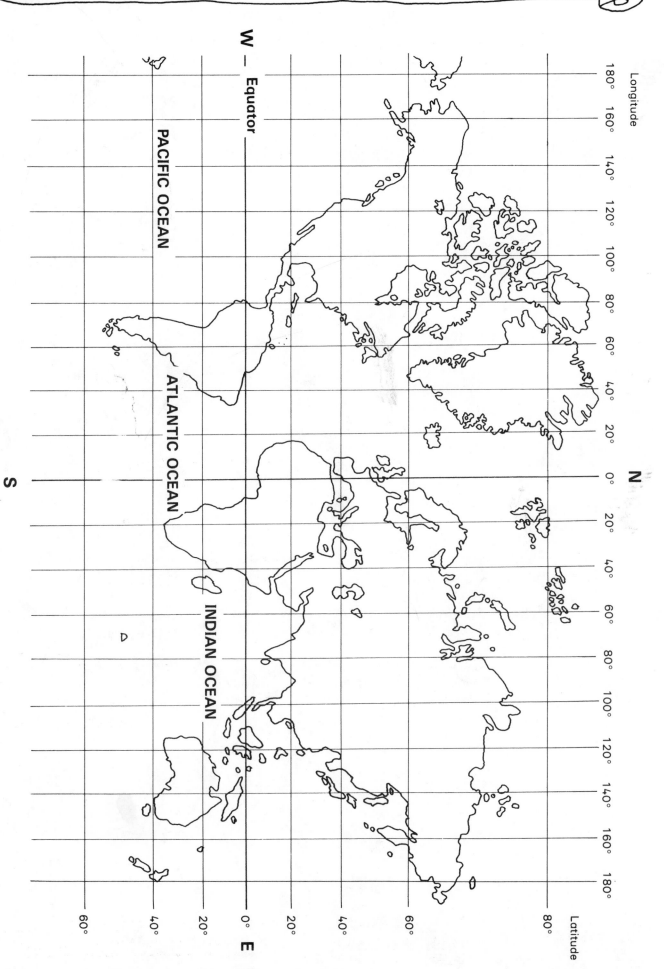